, line 2: — 3398 should be — 4398

, line 19: — 30.0 should be — 40.0

, last line: "iodine" should be "iodide"

, line 2: "iodine" should be "iodide"

, line 8 from bottom: $2H_2O$ should be $3H_2O$

line 3 from bottom: $Pb(BrO_3)$ should be $Pb(BrO_3)_2$

, line 5: $Tl(OH)$ should be $Tl(OH)_3$

, line 8 from bottom: ZnI^- should be ZnI^+

, line 8 from bottom: I should be I^-

, line 7: CuO_2^- should be $CuO_2^{--} + H_2O$

line 16: $Cu(IO_3)$ should be $Cu(IO_3)_2$

last line of footnote: 1530 (1950) should be 1550 (1951)

, line 9: $Ag(NH_3)+$ should be $Ag(NH_3)^+$

, line 6 from bottom: PtI_4^{--} should be $2PtI_4^{--}$

, line 8 from bottom: — 1.78 should be — 1.68

, line 13: $Rh + 3H_2O =$ etc. should be $2Rh + 3H_2O =$

, line 16: $2IrO_2 + Ir$ should be $3IrO_2 + Ir$

, line 1 following Basic Solution: 0.72 should be 0.73 and — 0.14 should be — 0.17

, line 11: CNS^- should be $3CNS^-$

, line 3: $HOsO_6^-$ should be $HOsO_5^-$

, line 5: ca 1.5 should be ca — 1.5

line 13: H_2O should be $2H_2O$

line 6 from bottom: $Mn(C_2O_4)_3$ should be $Mn(C_2O_4)_3^{---}$

, line 9: $2H^+$ should be H^+

line 10: H_2O should be $2H_2O$

, line 21: MoO_4 should be MoO_3

, line 2 from bottom: (1.25) should be (1.05)

, line 5 from bottom: — 0.26 should be — 0.274

, line 4 from bottom: (0.86) should be (0.89)

, line 7: 1.56 should be 1.53

, line 9 from bottom: $2H_2O$ should be H_2O

, line 6: 2.03 should be 2.07

, line 8: 2.03 should be 2.07

, line 16: iodide should be iodate

line 17: $2BrO_3^-$ should be $2IO_3^-$

, line 4 from bottom: $Cu - Cu^{++}$ should be $Ca - Ca^{++}$

, line 6 from bottom: K_2CO should be K_2CO_3

Page 8, lines 9 and 11: 51,170 shoul

Page 37, line 12: 1014 should be 954

Page 40, line 12: − 1.52 should be −

Page 47, line 3: 23.3 should be 2316

 line 4: 5.4 should be − 4.54

 line 3 from bottom: − 55.5 s

Page 49, line 3: 34.8 should be 34.69

Page 57, line 24: − 34.3 should be −

Page 62, line 10 from bottom: − 30,9(

Page 66, last line: − 123,900 should

Page 74, line 5: $6e^-$ should be $4e^-$

Page 78, line 12: 103e should be 10e

 line 20: − 5 kcal. should be

Page 80, line 11: − 51,800 should be

Page 84, line 11: − 56 should be − ǝ

Page 86, line 17: $TeO(OH_2)(c)$ shoul

Page 92, line 14: − 39.71 should be

 line 21: 2.46 should be 2.06

 line 26: − 2.34 should be −

 last line: − 12.26 should be

Page 95, line 14 from bottom: − 37.5

 line 12 from bottom: − 0.83$

 line 9 from bottom: − 0.496

Page 96, line 21: − 61.7 should be −

Page 97, line 13: 6.67 should be 6.45

 line 6 from bottom: − 118.7

Page 103, line 8: − 202 should be −

 line 19: − 37.65 should be

Page 104, line 3: − 1.41 should be −

 line 7: − 0.496 should be

Page 108, line 12: $HP_2O_7^{---}$ shoul

 line 13: HP_2O^{---} should

Page 111, line 15 from bottom: 1.82 s

Page 115, line 6 from bottom: − 45.5

 line 5 from bottom: $As_2S_3^-$

Page 116, line 2: AsS_2^{--} should be

Page 119, line 3: − 0.692 should be

Page 130, line 5 from bottom: 0.01 sh

Page 334, line 5 from bottom: 58.9 should be − 58.9

Page 336, line 5 from bottom of table: $CsCO_3$ should be Cs_2CO_3
        last line of table: $CsAl(SO_4)$ should be $CsAl(SO_4)_2$

Page 337, line 1 of table 83: − 1,720 should be − 1,920
                            − 4,000 should be 4,000
        line 2 of table 83: − 10,087 should be − 10,084
        line 4 of table 83: − 17,150 should be − 17,950
        line 5 of table 83: − 2,150 should be 7840

Page 340, line 5 of table 84: $As = As^+ + e^-$ should be $Cs = Cs^+ + e^-$

Page 341, line 22 of table 84: $H_3PO_3 = H_3PO_4 + 2H^+ + 2e^-$ should be
                            $H_2O + H_2PO_3 = H_3PO_4 + 2H^+ + 2e^-$

Page 389, right column, line 7 from bottom: Phosphorous should be
                            Phosphorus

THE OXIDATION STATES
OF THE ELEMENTS AND
THEIR POTENTIALS IN
AQUEOUS SOLUTIONS

Second Edition

BY

WENDELL M. LATIMER

PRENTICE-HALL, INC.
Englewood Cliffs, N. J.

QD
561
.L35
ΙΙ 1952

Preface to Second Edition

In the *Second Edition* the author has sought to extend the summarization of those thermodynamic data which are of special significance in the interpretation of inorganic chemistry. For each element the heats of formation, free energies of formation and entropies have been tabulated for all important compounds. Many of the free energies are based upon estimated entropy values and a discussion has been given in the Appendix of the methods by which accurate estimations of entropy values may be made.

The author has been gratified by the extensive use of the potential diagrams, which were introduced in the *First Edition,* and such diagrams are now given for all the elements which have more than one oxidation state. A discussion of the use of these diagrams in the interpretation of the chemistry of an element is given in Chapter I. Several hundred new potential values and equilibrium constants also have been added.

The treatment of reaction rates and reaction mechanisms has been extended, but the author has not been able to expand these topics as fully as he would like. The chemistry of uranium, neptunium, plutonium and americium has been greatly amplified and the actinide elements are treated in a new chapter.

For the great majority of substances, the U. S. Bureau of Standards values for reaction heats have been employed. In many cases the Bureau of Standards values for the free energies differ by only a few small calories from the author's previous values. In all such cases, the Bureau of Standards values are adapted for the sake of conformity and to avoid unnecessary complications in secondary calculations employing these free energies. In all tables the Bureau of Standards values are indicated by italics.

Since the book has been employed as a text for courses in Advanced Inorganic Chemistry, a set of study questions has been included in the Appendix.

The author is indebted to the many chemists who have written suggestions and corrections and to his colleagues at the University of California, especially to Dr. R. E. Connick and Dr. Z. Z. Hugus.

WENDELL M. LATIMER

Preface to the First Edition

The most convenient method of ascertaining the relative heights of two mountains is generally by reference to a table of measured altitudes. In order to use the table, it is not necessary to understand the principles of triangulation by which the altitudes have been determined. So, also, a table of the energies of the elements in their various oxidation states may be used by one with a very elementary knowledge of thermodynamics to answer many of the qualitative questions involved in the interpretation of inorganic chemistry.

In making this summary of existing data, the author has adopted the point of view of one interested in the chemistry of the various elements, rather than the point of view of one whose interest is largely in thermodynamics as a science. The author hopes that readers of the latter class, who are disappointed at the frequent inclusion of approximate data, will find in these obvious shortcomings an incentive for careful investigations in the near future. Much of the older work should have been recalculated by modern methods, but the labor involved is beyond the capacity of a single author.

The free energies of the oxidation-reduction couples, taken with reference to the hydrogen couple, have been expressed as volts per equivalent, since this affords the simplest comparison of the relative driving power of the various couples. However, for completed oxidation-reduction reactions, the free energies have been given in calories, as the number of equivalents of electricity is sometimes ambiguous. Solubility products and the dissociation constants of weak acids, bases, and complex ions have been included whenever the data were available.

The author, in calculating many new free energies from reaction heats, has drawn largely upon his own experimental work on the entropies of solids and aqueous ions. Our present knowledge of the entropy values permits the estimation of many entropies from the values of similar substances, and these estimates have frequently been employed in third-law calculations to obtain approximate reaction potentials.

Potentials have been given for many couples which are not thermodynamically reversible. These values, of course, cannot be used in equilibrium reasoning. However, these potentials are of value in indicating the minimum energy which must be employed to accomplish the oxidation or reduction, and they often give considerable information regarding the possible reaction mechanisms and the cause of the slowness of the reactions.

In some cases it would be valuable to list potentials for couples at 1 M concentration, rather than list the $E°$ values. However, these molal potentials are not so useful as one might at first think. They can be used accurately only at 1 M concentration; and, if an approximate value is desired, the $E°$ without corrections for the activity might as well be used.

References have been given for all values employed. These references may usually be consulted for additional references to older works. The author has endeavored to include in his references all works published up to 1938.

Some mention should be made of the author's attempt to avoid the confusion existing with regard to the use of the term *valence*. This term has been restricted to mean, in the organic chemistry sense, the number of bonds (electron pairs) which an atom shares with other atoms. Such a usage renders the terms *covalence* and *coördination number* unnecessary but requires additional nomenclature to designate the charge upon an atom. In many cases this charge is a readily determinable number as, for example, the charge of -1 on chloride ion. This charge will be called the *polar number*. In a large number of compounds the polar number of each atom cannot be readily determined experimentally, but a fair approximation is obtained by assuming that the two electrons of a bond are shared equally between the two atoms. On this basis the charge upon the sulfur atom in sulfate is $+2$ and that upon each oxygen is -1. The term *formal polar number* has been suggested for the charge estimated in this manner.

However, for the purpose of classification, a still more arbitrary method of assigning values to the charges upon the atoms of a compound has proved extremely useful. As an example, we may again use the sulfate ion. This method assumes that each oxygen has a charge of -2, which then gives a charge of $+6$ to the sulfur. These assumptions not only simplify the classification of compounds but are also valuable in the interpretation of oxidation-reduction reactions. Thus, the $+6$ charge on the sulfur may be correlated with the six electrons involved in the half-reaction for the oxidation of sulfur to sulfate,

$$S + 4H_2O = 8H^+ + SO_4^{--} + 6e^-.$$

Similar half-reactions may be written for the oxidation (or reduction) of any free element to any of its compounds, and the number of electrons involved in the reaction may be used to define the oxidation number or oxidation state of the element.

To summarize the illustration of nomenclature for the sulfate example, we may state: the valence of the sulfur is four; the polar number is unknown, but the formal polar number is $+2$; and the oxidation state is $+6$.

The author owes much to the spirit of coöperation which has been so carefully fostered in this department by Professor Gilbert N. Lewis. In the author's opinion there is no man who has such a complete understanding of the mechanism of inorganic reactions as does Professor William C. Bray, and he is especially indebted to Professor Bray for the advice so willingly given on many problems. The author wishes to thank both the many graduate students who have read and criticized the manuscript and Dr. George G. Manov for his recalculation of many of the free energies.

WENDELL M. LATIMER

Contents